THE
NEW POTTY

BY GINA AND MERCER MAYER

For Margie Gurkin
A.K.A. "Hot Rod Harry"

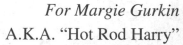

SCHOLASTIC INC.
New York Toronto London Auckland
Sydney Mexico City New Delhi Hong Kong

12 11 10 9 8 7 6 5 4 3 2 1   10 11 12 13 14 15/0 • Printed in the U.S.A.   40 • First Scholastic printing, October 2010

I am a big boy. I know how to use the potty. I have underpants with skateboards on them.

My little sister is still a baby.
She wears diapers.

I like to play with my sister. But sometimes she smells funny and Mom has to change her diapers.

One day Mom said, "It's time for
Little Sister to use a potty."
I thought that was a good idea.

We went to the store to get a potty chair
for my sister. Mom picked out a pink one.

When we got home, my little sister
wanted to carry the new potty
inside by herself.

But she wouldn't sit on it. She cried instead.
Mom said, "She's scared." I knew that.

So I sat on the potty first.
Then my sister wasn't scared anymore.

I got her a book to read. Then she didn't want to get off the potty at all.

Mom took the potty downstairs so my sister could sit on it while she watched TV.

That was weird.

My sister sat on her potty while she ate dinner.

Later she sat her doll on the potty.

She tried to sit my monkey on it, but I wouldn't let her.

That night my little sister slept with the potty beside her bed.

In the morning, Mom sat my little sister on the potty without her diaper. My sister read her book. Then she used the potty.

Mom hugged her while she was still sitting on the potty, but I didn't.

Then Mom put new underpants on my little sister.
"You look so cute," Mom said.
I didn't think she looked any cuter than me.

We played in the sandbox. I noticed that some of the sand was wet, so I called Mom.

While Mom was doing laundry,
my little sister said, "Potty."

Mom asked *me* to take her.

My sister missed the potty and got the floor wet. We called Mom.

The next time my little sister went to
the potty, she did it just right.
We were proud of her.

Now that my little sister can use the potty,
Mom and Dad say she is a big girl.

But I think she still acts like a baby.

Sometimes.